Letterland

24 pages

Phonics Practice 1

Decodable text

Contains:
s, ă, t, p, ĭ, n, m, d, g, ŏ, c, k, ck, ě, ŭ, r

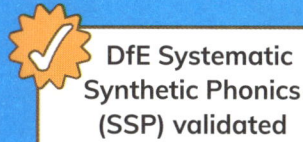
DfE Systematic Synthetic Phonics (SSP) validated

Name:

S s - Sammy Snake

1. Trace over Sammy Snake's letter shapes and say his sound.

2. Write over the dotted letters. Then complete the lines.

3. Colour the pictures that start with Sammy Snake's sound.

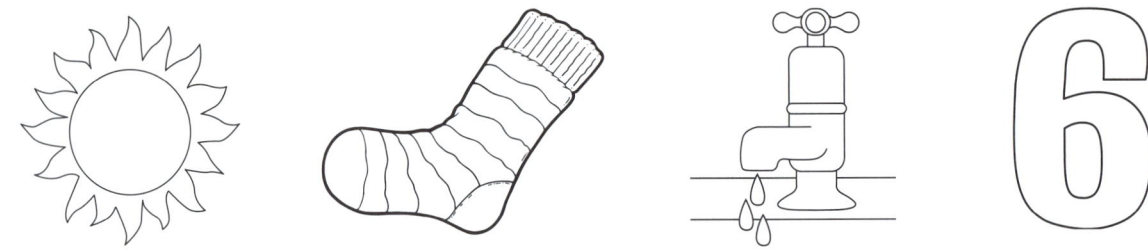

4. Join the pictures that start with Sammy Snake's sound to his letter.

A a - Annie Apple

1. Trace over Annie Apple's letter shapes and say her sound.

2. Write over the dotted letters. Then complete the lines.

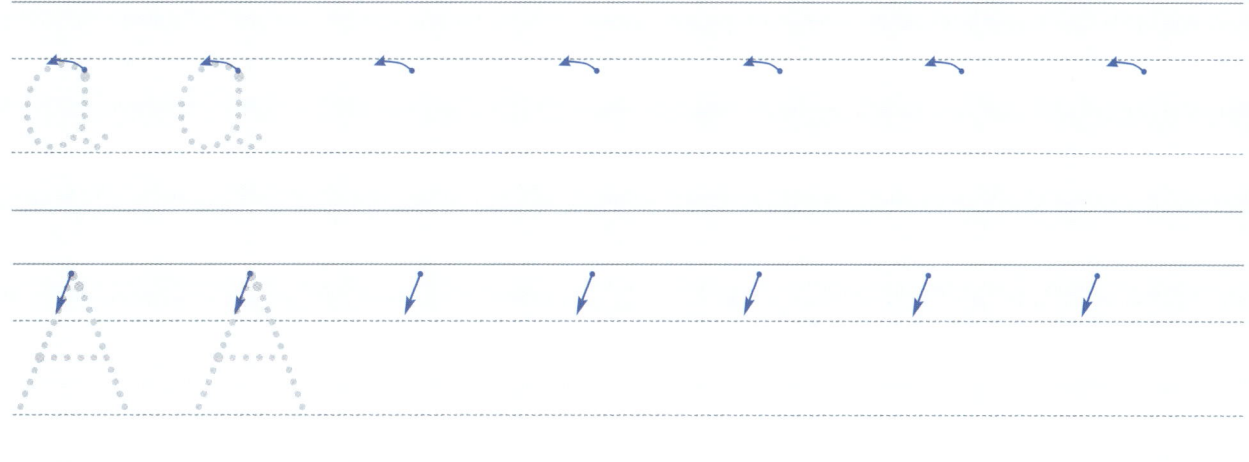

3. Join the pictures that start with Annie Apple's sound to her letter.

4. Colour the pictures that start with her sound.

T t - Talking Tess

1. Trace over Talking Tess's letter shapes and say her sound.

2. Write over the dotted letters. Then complete the lines.

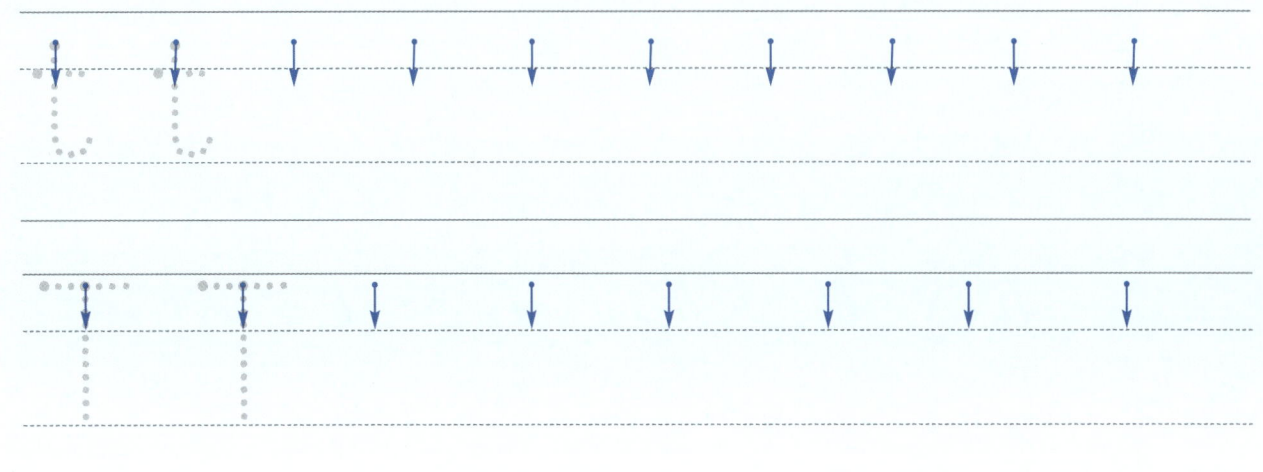

3. Colour the pictures that start with Talking Tess's sound.

4. Write her letter by each object that starts with her sound.

P p - Peter Puppy

1. Trace over Peter Puppy's letter shapes and say his sound.

2. Write over the dotted letters. Then complete the lines.

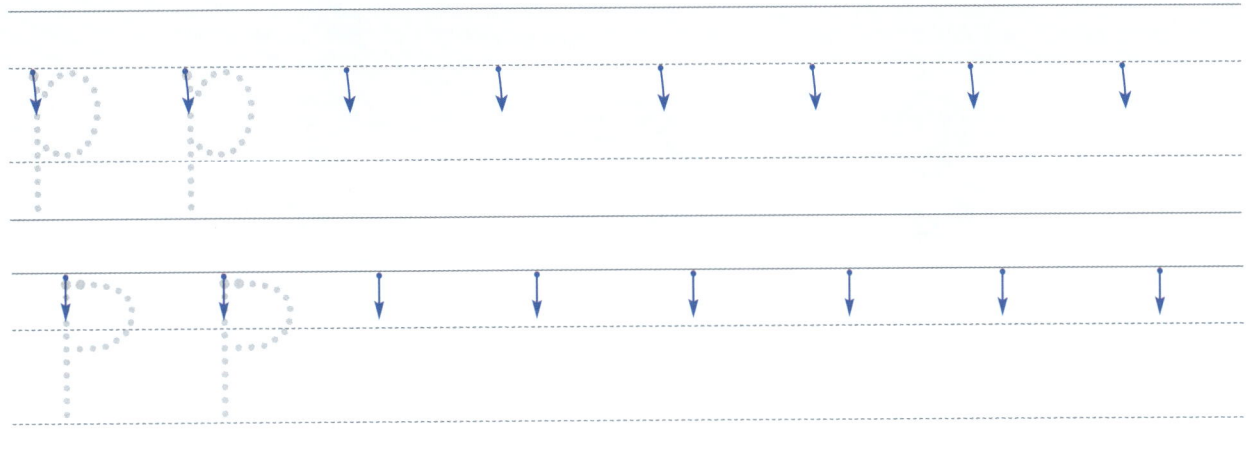

3. Colour the pictures that start with Peter Puppy's sound.

4. Write his letter by each object that starts with his sound.

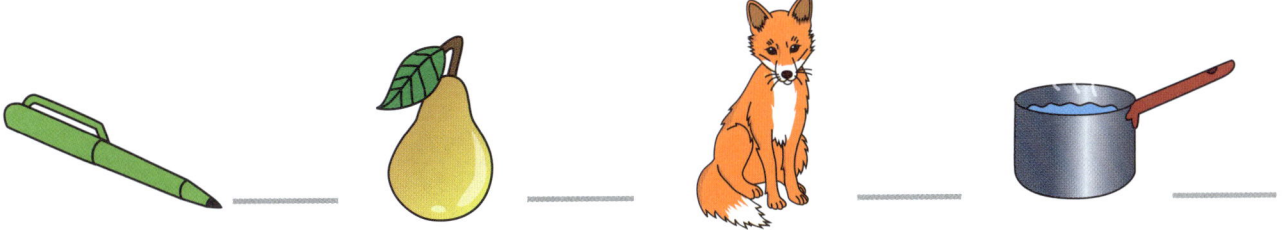

Blending

1. Finger-trace each letter as you say its sound.

2. Touch the dot under each letter as you say its sound.

3. Say the sounds again but a little faster.

4. Now blend the sounds to read the word.

5. Circle the picture that matches the word above.

Blending

1. Blend the sounds to read the word. Circle the picture that matches it.

sat

pat

tap

sap

2. Write the four words from above. Then read them aloud.

sat

pat

I i - Impy Ink

1. Trace over Impy Ink's letter shapes and say his sound.

2. Write over the dotted letters. Then complete the lines.

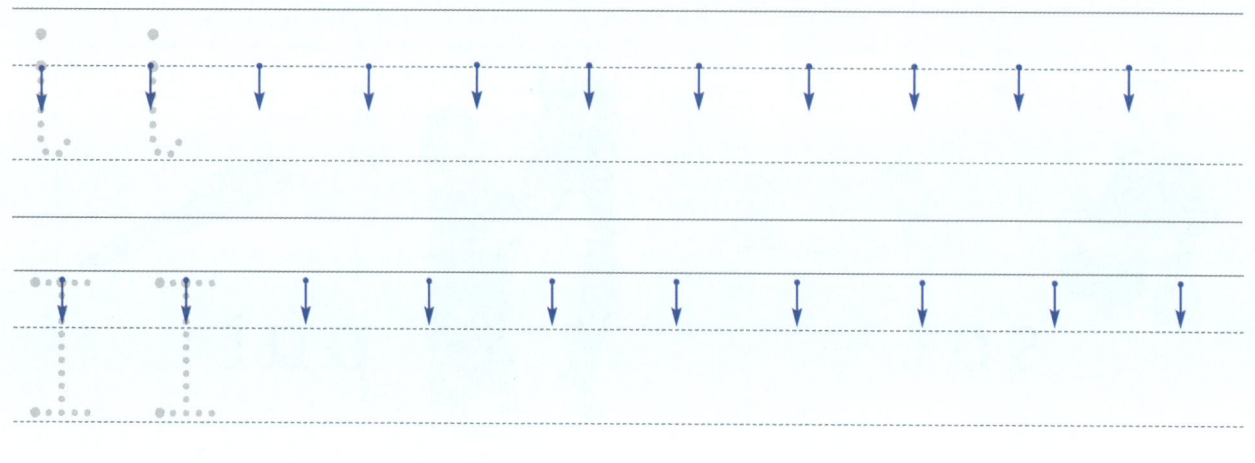

3. Colour the pictures that start with Impy Ink's sound.

4. Write his letter by each object that starts with his sound.

N n - Noisy Nick

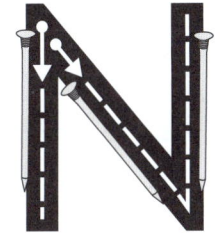

1. Trace over Noisy Nick's letter shapes and say his sound.

2. Write over the dotted letters. Then complete the lines.

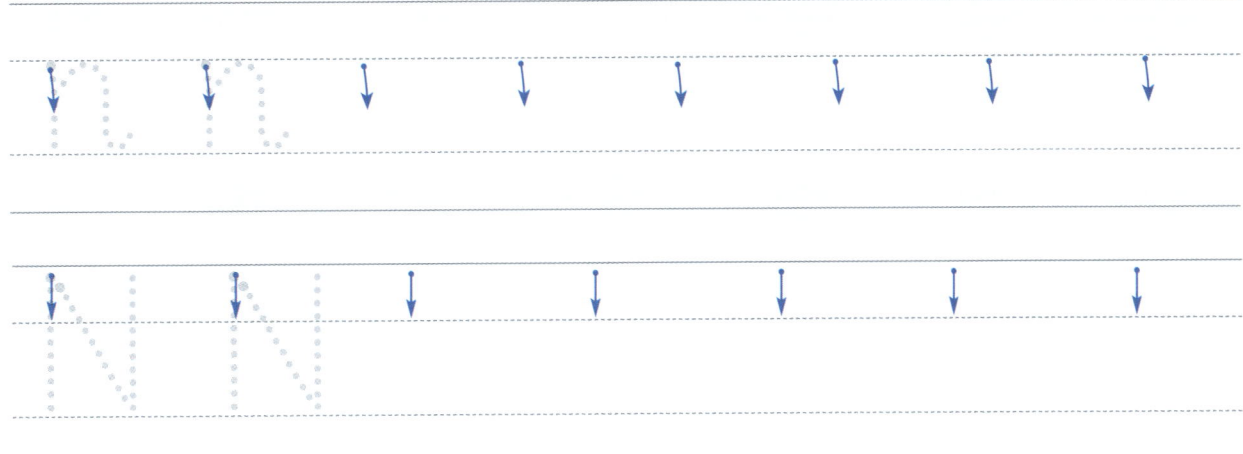

3. Colour the pictures that start with Noisy Nick's sound.

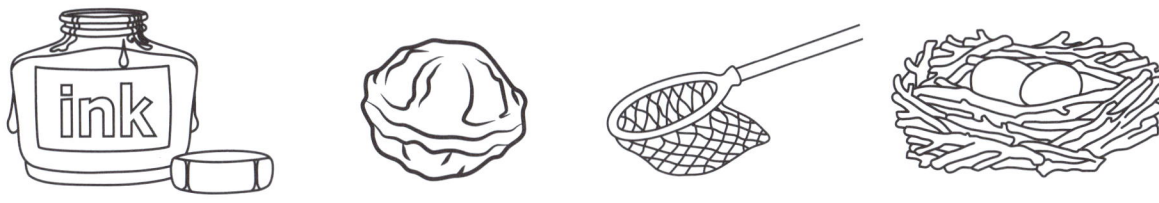

4. Join the pictures that start with Noisy Nick's sound to his letter.

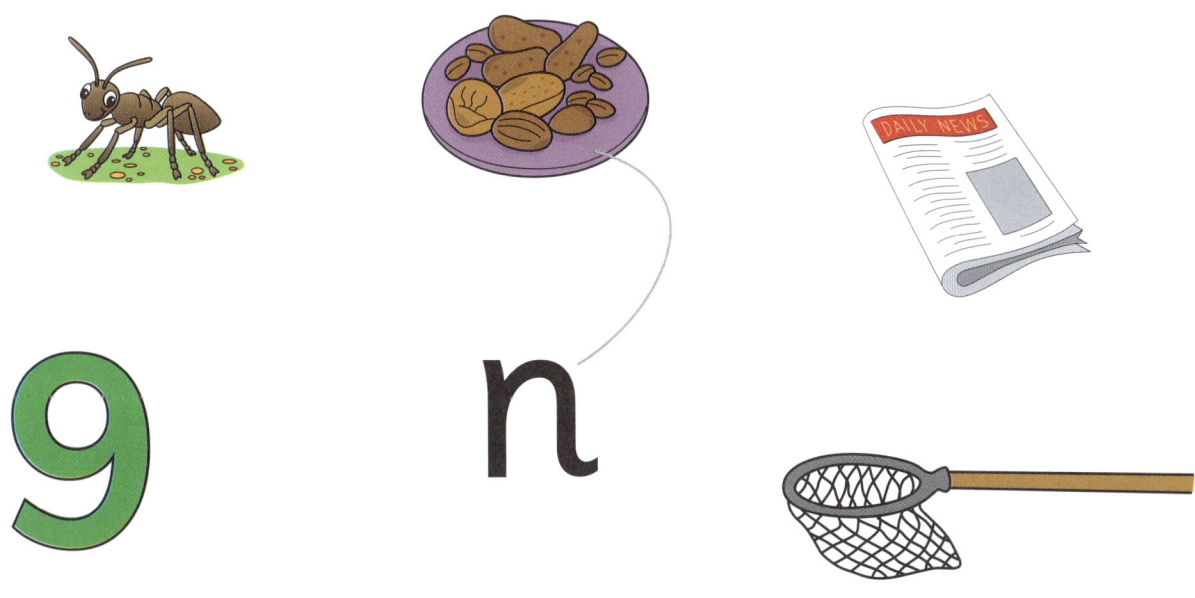

M m - Munching Mike

1. Trace over Munching Mike's letter shapes and say his sound.

2. Write over the dotted letters. Then complete the lines.

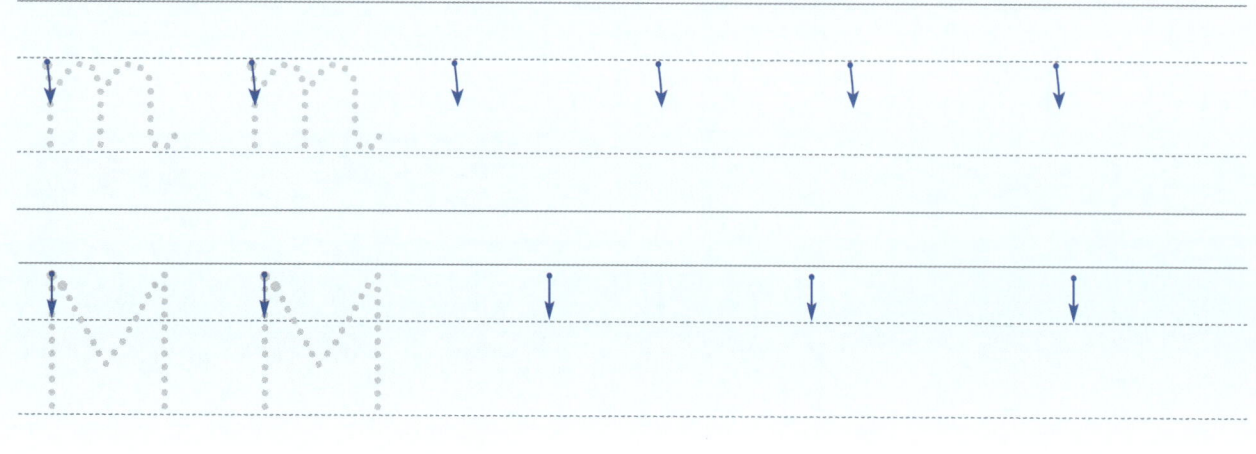

3. Colour the pictures that start with Munching Mike's sound.

 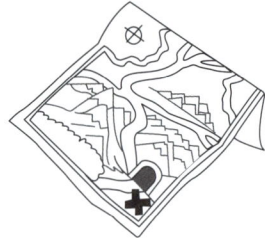  

4. Join the pictures that start with Munching Mike's sound to his letter.

D d - Dippy Duck

1. Trace over Dippy Duck's letter shapes and say her sound.

2. Write over the dotted letters. Then complete the lines.

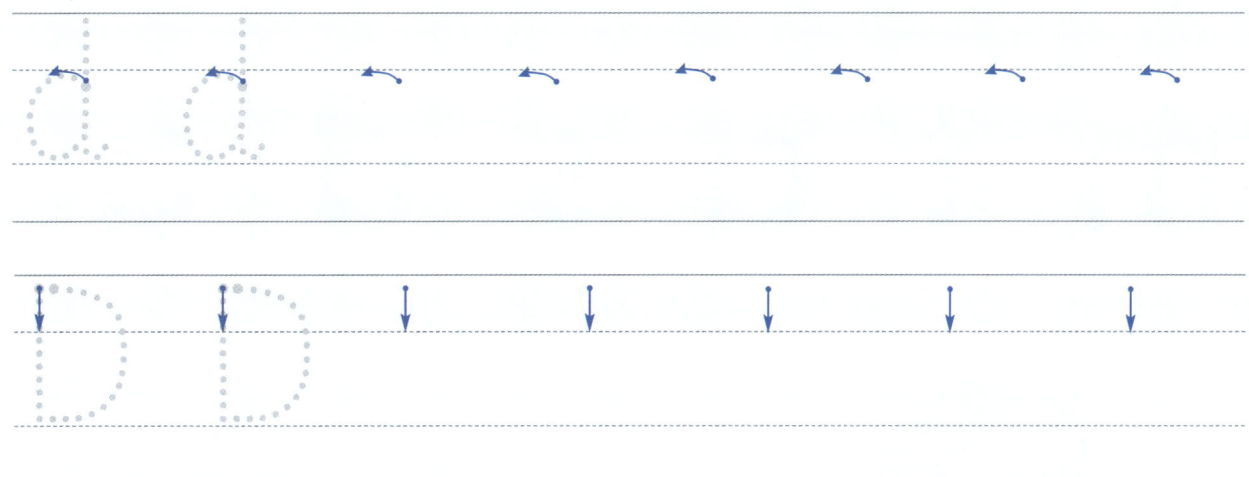

3. Colour the pictures that start with her sound.

4. Join the pictures that start with Dippy Duck's sound to her letter.

11

Segmenting

1. Use these letters to write the words for the pictures.

m t a s d a

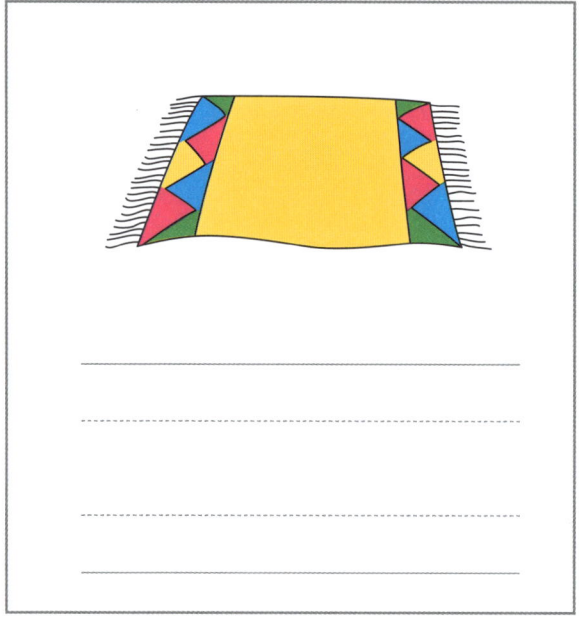

2. Draw a line to join the correct word to this picture.

dad   mat

sit   sip

Segmenting

1. Stretch the pictured words using the Rubber Band Trick, and write the word by the picture.

2. Read the sentence. Then copy it.

It is a tin.

It is a tin.

Sometimes Sammy Snake likes to take a little snooze in words. /zzz/

G g - Golden Girl

1. Trace over Golden Girl's letter shapes and say her sound.

2. Write over the dotted letters. Then complete the lines.

3. Colour the pictures that start with Golden Girl's sound.

4. Write her letter by each object that starts with her sound.

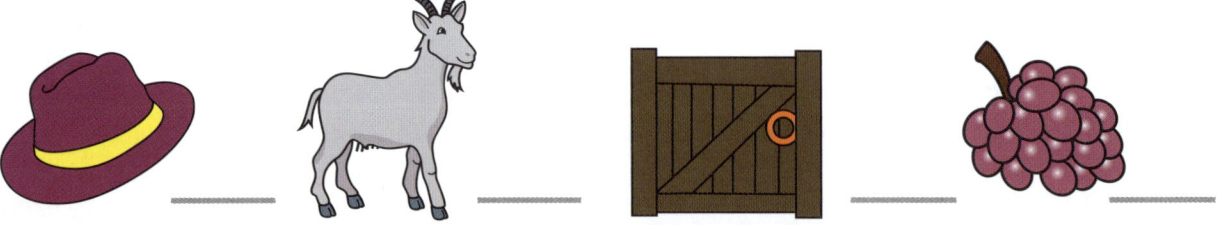

O o - Oscar Orange

1. Trace over Oscar Orange's letter shapes and say his sound.

2. Write over the dotted letters. Then complete the lines.

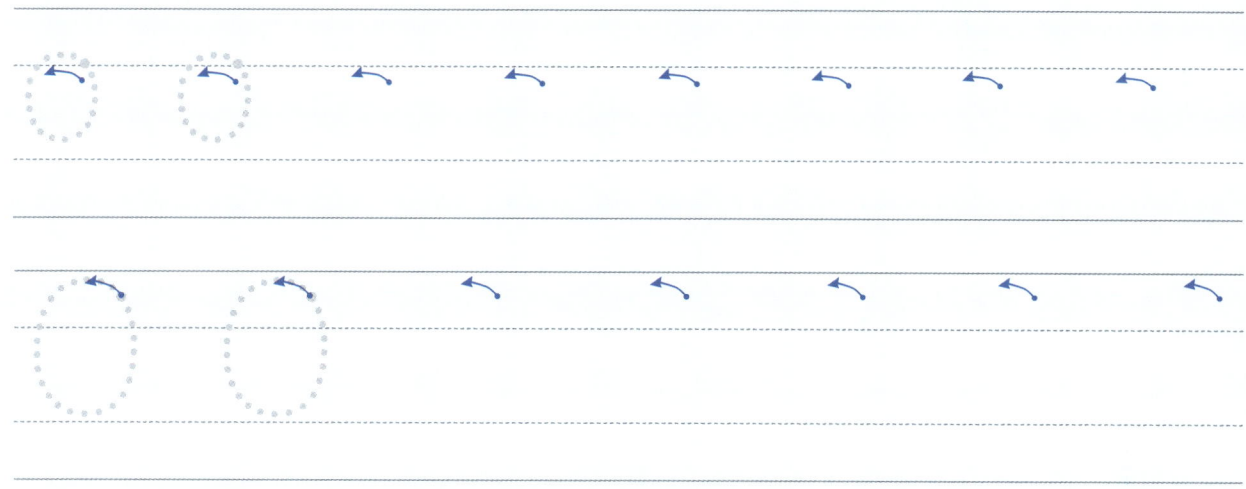

3. Colour the pictures that start with Oscar Orange's sound.

4. Join the pictures that start with Oscar Orange's sound to his letter.

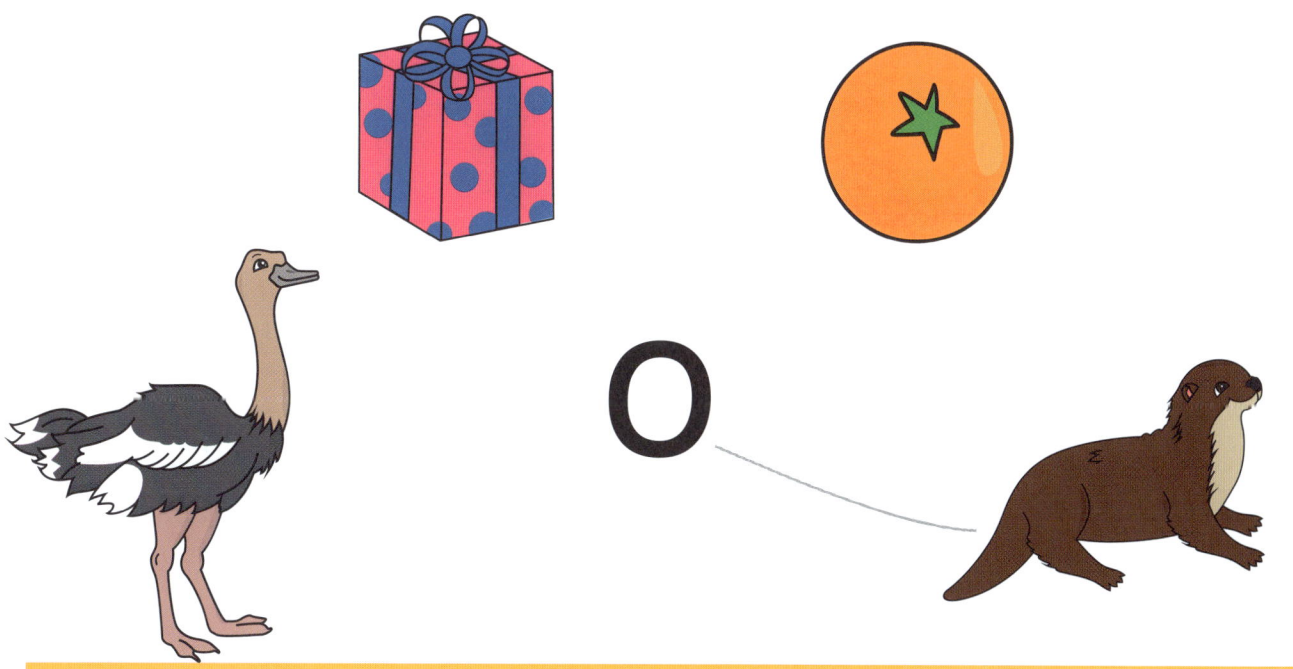

C c - Clever Cat

1. Trace over Clever Cat's letter shapes and say her sound.

2. Write over the dotted letters. Then complete the lines.

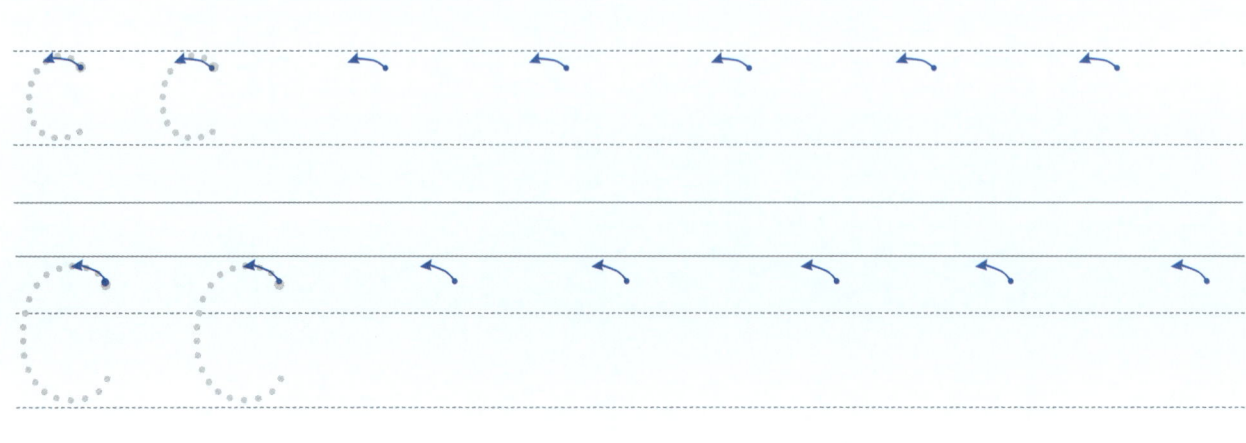

3. Colour the pictures that start with Clever Cat's sound.

4. Write her letter by each animal that starts with her sound.

K k - Kicking King

1. Trace over Kicking King's letter shapes and say his sound.

2. Write over the dotted letters. Then complete the lines.

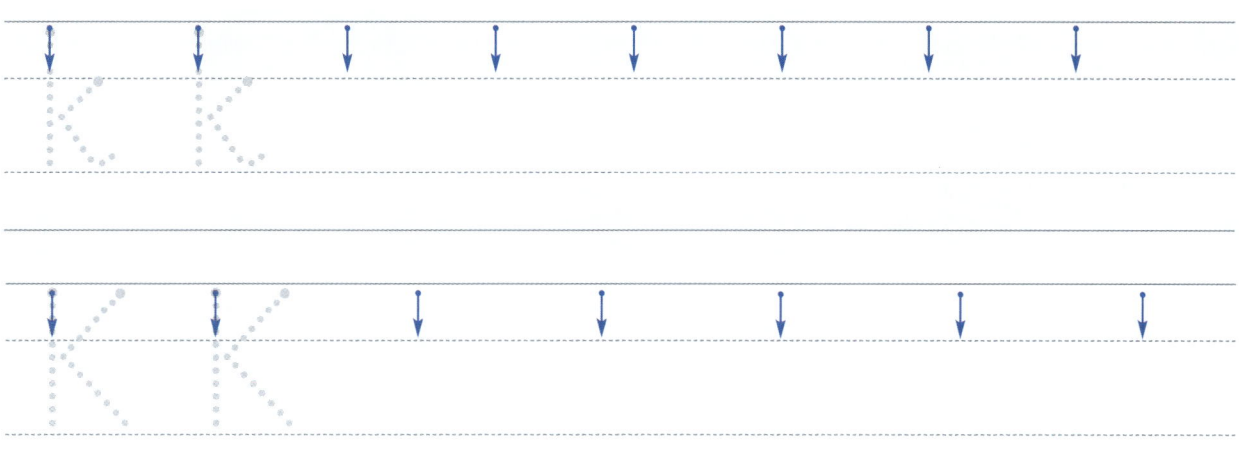

3. Colour the kites containing pictures that start with Kicking King's sound.

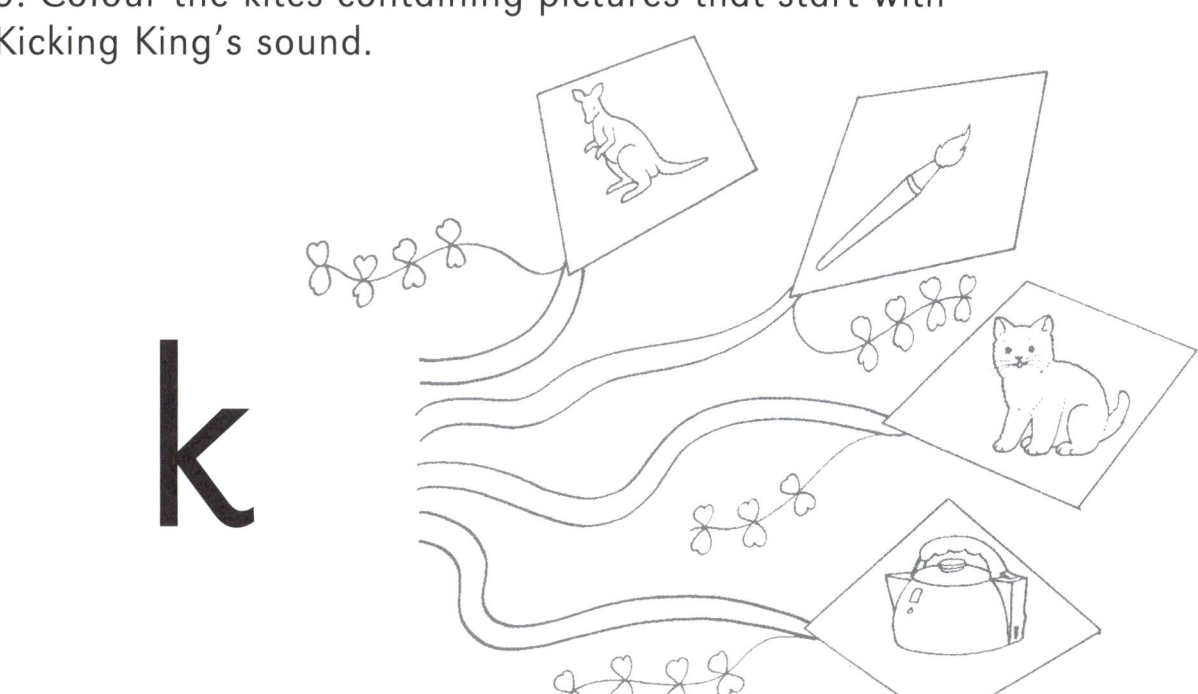

4. Write his letter by each object that starts with his sound.

17

ck as in duck Clever Cat and Kicking King

1. Read the words. Circle the word that matches each picture.

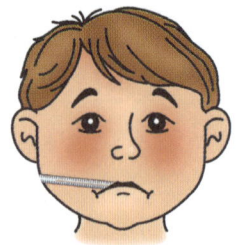

sack   back   sat   sick

dock   sock   kick   kiss

2. Stretch and segment each pictured word using the Rubber Band Trick. Then write the letters on the lines.

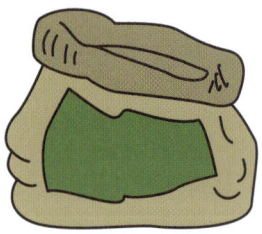

18

E e - Eddy Elephant

1. Trace over Eddy Elephant's letter shapes and say his sound.

2. Write over the dotted letters. Then complete the lines.

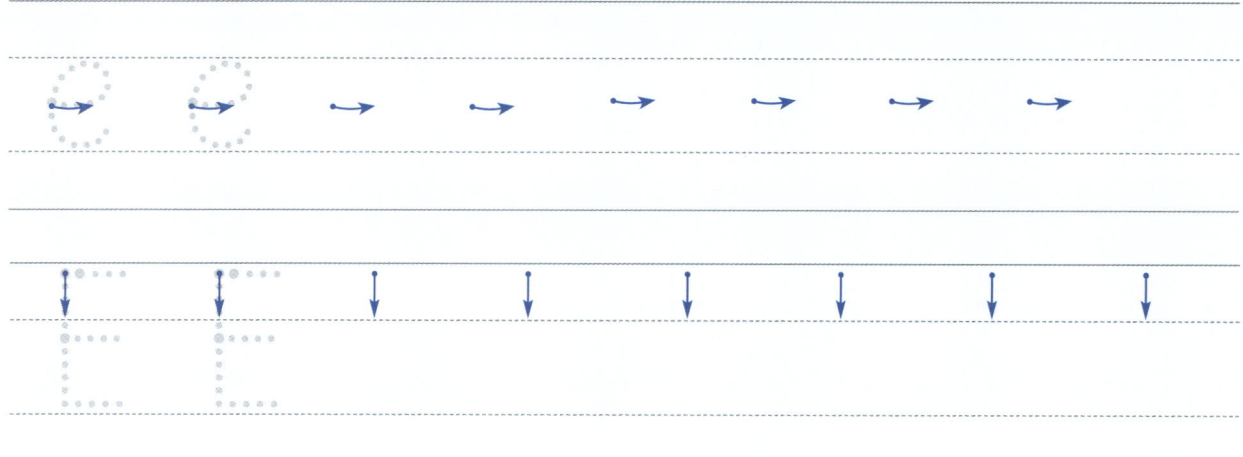

3. Colour the pictures that start with Eddy Elephant's sound.

4. Write his letter by each object that starts with his sound.

U u - Uppy Umbrella

1. Trace over Uppy Umbrella's letter shapes and say her sound.

2. Write over the dotted letters. Then complete the lines.

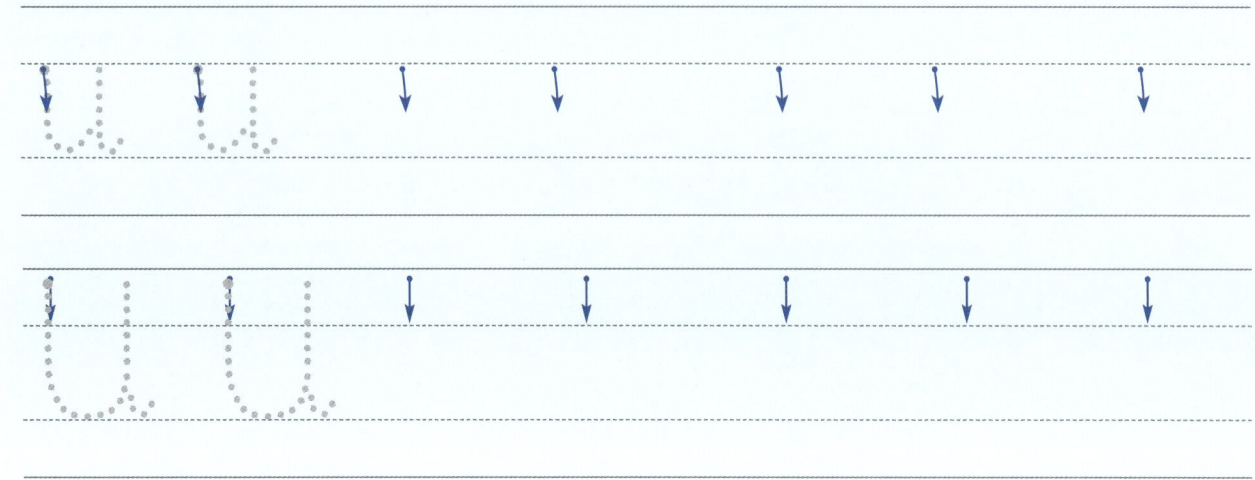

3. Colour the pictures that start with her sound.

   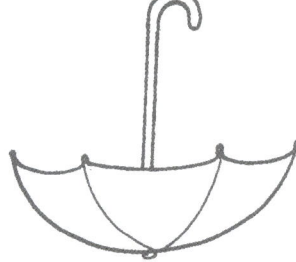

4. Join the pictures that start with Uppy Umbrella's sound to her letter.

R r - Red Robot

1. Trace over Red Robot's letter shapes and say his sound.

2. Write over the dotted letters. Then complete the lines.

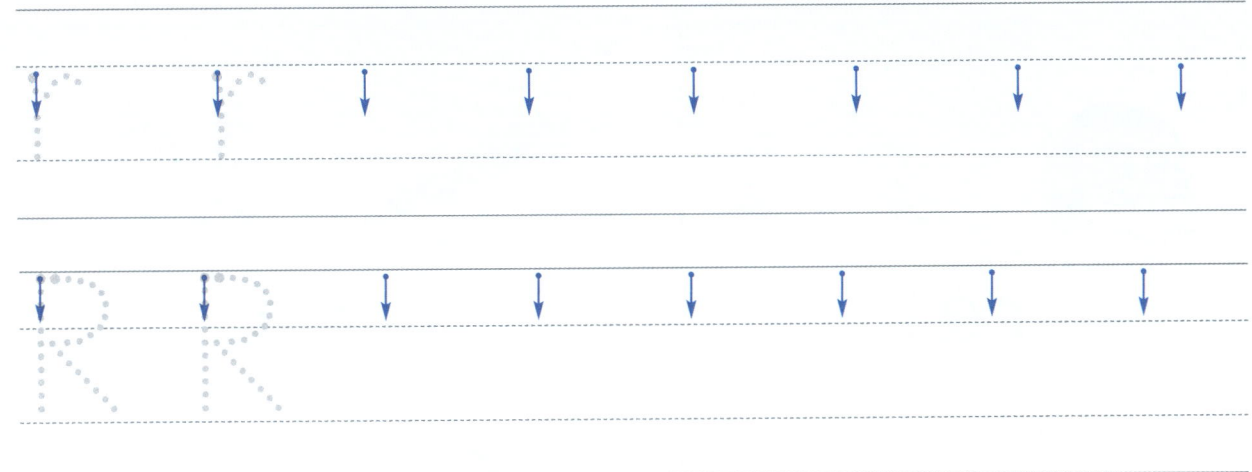

3. Write Red Robot's letter by each object that starts with his sound.

4. Colour the pictures that start with Red Robot's sound.

21

Blending and segmenting

1. Blend the sounds to read the words. Circle the pictures that match the words.

rat

ten

sun

run

2. Stretch and segment each pictured word using the Rubber Band Trick. Then write the letters on the lines.

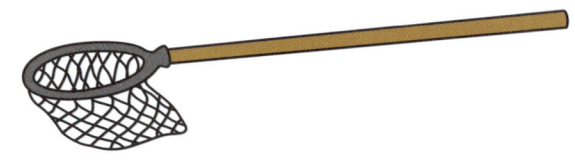

___ ___ ___   ___ ___ ___

Write

Write the missing letters to spell the word for each picture.

od ad	eg og	an ad
 d___	 p___	 s___
eg ug	ed id	op ap
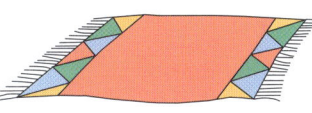 r___	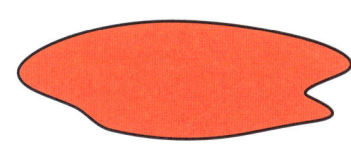 r___	 p___
an in	an in	ip ap
 p___	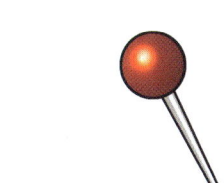 p___	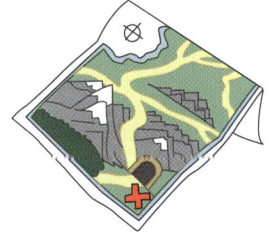 m___

How to use this book

On each page, read the instructions to the children. Name all the pictures with them. Let them try and read all the words in the exercises themselves, as they are decodable.

Letter sounds

Many of the activities in this book rely on knowing the letter sounds **satp inmd gock ck eur**. Make sure children use the Letterland Sound Trick to discover the letter's sound:

Just START to say any Letterlander's name, and catch the very first sound that comes out of your mouth. That sound is actually the sound that letter makes in words.
For example: Sammy Snake 'sss...' (not 'suh' or 'ess'), Annie Apple 'a...' (not 'ay'),
Talking Tess 't...' (not 'tuh' or 'tee')

Letter shapes

By making sure children start with the right movement pathway for each letter, you will be ensuring that on moving to joined-up handwriting the transition will be smooth and easy. If young children are allowed to form letters their own way, incorrect habits quickly become deep-rooted and can be very difficult to correct later.

Upper/lowercase pairs

Ask the children to look carefully at the differences in the size and shape of each upper/lowercase letter pair. The need to make this judgement for themselves prepares them for writing without lines.

It is important to use this workbook:
- when children are not tired
- when there are no background distractions
- for short periods of time
- with plenty of praise and encouragement.

Left-hander   Right-hander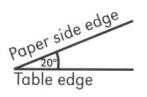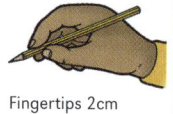

Fingertips 4cm from tip of pencil

Elbows off the table
Feet on floor

Paper side edge / Table edge

Chair slightly tilted
Feet on floor

Fingertips 2cm from tip of pencil

You may also like:

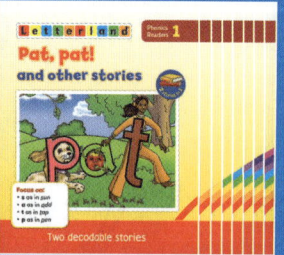 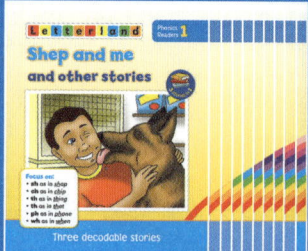

See our full range at: **www.letterland.com**

Published by Letterland International Ltd,
8/10 South Street, Epsom, Surrey, KT18 7PF, UK
© Letterland International 2021
10 9 8 7 6 5 4 3 2

ISBN: 978-1-78248-551-3
Product Code: TP65

LETTERLAND™ is a trademark of Letterland International Ltd.
Printed in China.

All rights reserved. No part of this publication may be reproduced, stored in a retrieval system, or transmitted in any form or by any means, electronic, mechanical, photocopying, recording or otherwise, without the prior permission of the Publisher or a licence permitting restricted copying in the United Kingdom issued by the Copyright Licensing Agency Ltd, 90 Tottenham Court Road, London W1P 0LP. British Library Cataloguing in Publication Data. A catalogue record for this book is available from the British Library.

Sassoon Infant is a typeface designed for children learning to read and write.
© Adrian Williams Design Ltd

Written and designed by Lisa Holt
Consultant: Lyn Wendon, originator of Letterland

Please Note: These practice books match the teaching order in the Letterland *Phonics Teacher's Guide*.

For those who wish to follow a different teaching order the practice books can be used flexibly.

Code: TP65
ISBN 978-1-78248-551-3

Letterland Child-friendly phonics